Stories for Thin

Lynn Hutchinson

HODDER AND STOUGHTON
LONDON SYDNEY AUCKLAND TORONTO

British Library Cataloguing in Publication Data

Hutchinson, Lynn
  Stories for thinking.
  1. Readers——1950–
  I. Title
  428.6   PE1119

ISBN 0-340-35395-3

First published 1984

Typeset in 12/14 pt Univers Medium (Monophoto) by Butler and Tanner Ltd.
Printed in Great Britain for Hodder and Stoughton Educational,
a division of Hodder and Stoughton Ltd,
Mill Road, Dunton Green, Sevenoaks, Kent,
by Butler and Tanner Ltd, Frome and London

Contents

Preface

The stories which unfold in this book have been divided into episodes and written to involve the reader actively at every stage. In order to answer the questions following each episode, higher-order levels of comprehension are required.

None of the questions requires literal answers. All demand anticipatory or predictive responses, or discrimination between facts and opinions. Justified generalisations might be elicited, or the perception of various relationships in time and space encouraged. Reading between and beyond the lines is necessary because many of the actions and ideas are implied or inferred. Mental image-making is required, as is the interpretation of figurative language. Logical judgments and conclusions supported by argument are often called for. The clear and logical stories are designed to provide motivation to engage in these reading and thinking skills.

In practice, this directed reading activity works best when each episode is followed by group discussion. The questions serve as a guide and starting point. Active involvement through discussion leads to gains in understanding and clear thinking. Thus speaking and listening aspects of language are united with reading and thinking, and become a fundamental part of the total activity.

Story 1 Deep Water

The children were having fun in the water. Sam was knee deep, enjoying the feeling of the waves splashing against his legs. As the waves rolled forward, he could feel the sand under his feet being pulled back, such was the strength of the undertow. His sisters were in up to their waists, jumping as the waves broke against them. Because the beach shelved so quickly, all three children were quite close to each other.

The children's parents were sitting high up the beach in the dunes. Their father was sleeping, and their mother was reading the paper. Sam thought they fussed too much. They were always predicting awful accidents which never happened. At least, they hadn't so far . . .

1   What do you think the family could be doing here?
2   How does Sam know there is an undertow?
3   The writer mentions that the three children are quite close to each other. Why might he bother to describe that?
4   Why do you think the parents chose to sit in the sand dunes?
5   What might the parents be fussing about on this day?
6   What do you think might happen next?

Turn to page 8

Story 2 **The Flood**

Suddenly the rain poured down. It danced off the roads and paths. It beat down on the roofs of houses. It drummed on the roof of the bungalow. The noise was very loud on the iron roof. It could even be heard over the music Peter was playing. He turned to his friend.

'You haven't got a coat with you. You'll have to wait till the rain goes off before you go home. It looks as if you are going to be wet, or late!'

Peter switched off the cassette player.

'Can you hear that noise?' he said. 'Listen.'

Together they listened to the sound of the rain. As well as the drumming sound, a rapid pattering and splashing could be heard.

1   What clues are there so far which give you an idea of what the story will be about?
2   Is Peter's friend more likely to be a boy or girl? Why?
3   If Peter's friend left for home now, what would he/she be in trouble for?
4   What time of year could it be? Why?
5   What do you think the new sound could be?
6   What do you think could happen next?

Turn to page 9

Story 3   **The Theft**

'Lend me your calculator, will you?' Simon asked James.

'You should get one of your own,' James replied.

'I will do, soon. I'm saving up,' said Simon. 'But I must check these answers before I give this work in.'

James bent down to take the calculator from his bag. He felt in the pocket. He took his books out, and his sports-gear, and then his writing materials. There was no calculator.

'It's gone,' James said, with a sinking heart. What would his parents say? He had only had it three weeks, since his birthday.

'Are you sure you packed it?' asked Simon.

'Yes,' said James. 'I remember putting it in last night. I haven't needed it today, until you asked. There's only one explanation.'

1   Why does Simon not have a calculator?
2   How do you think James came to get his calculator?
3   What do you think James's parents might say?
4   Why does what his parents say worry James?
5   What explanation do you think James has in mind?
6   What do you think will happen next?

Turn to page 10

Story 4   **In Trouble**

It was a cold January day. The wind was chill as it whistled through the bare branches of the trees. The few people in the park walked briskly. Only the children and dogs seemed cheerful. They ran about the play area and around the edges of the pond.

When it happened, there wasn't much of a splash.

The little girl floundered in the shallow water at the edge of the pond. Her feet were sinking in the mud. She lost her balance and sat down. Her two older sisters, not more than six or seven years old themselves, lay on the bank and caught her by the arms. They pulled her to the side and up the bank. No one had noticed.

1   What is different about the way the children and adults respond to the cold day?
2   What could the reasons be for there not being a big splash?
3   What danger is the little girl in?
4   What problems do the older sisters face now?
5   What would be the most responsible thing to do now?
6   What do you think will happen next?

Turn to page 11

Story 5   **Joe's Lorry**

Joe owned his own lorry. He made his living by picking up and delivering all types of loads. He moved anything from building materials to furniture, sacks of coal to potatoes. This afternoon he was on his way back from the market, where he had been delivering Christmas trees. He had been on the road since early in the morning as he had to load them first from where they had been cut down. As it began to get dark, Joe wondered what there would be for dinner. He was very hungry, thirsty, and tired. His arms and back ached. The traffic on the main road was heavy, and Joe decided to cut across a housing estate. A few minutes later, just as Joe was about to turn left, as he looked to his right he noticed smoke billowing about. It appeared to be coming from the ground floor of a house down the road.

1   What do you think this story is going to be about?
2   Why would anyone employ Joe and his lorry?
3   Why do you think Joe's arms and back ached?
4   What time would Joe's watch show?
5   How would smoke coming from the ground floor affect the rest of the house?
6   What do you think Joe will do next?

Turn to page 12

Story 6   **The Dig**

It was nearly tea-time. As he filled his bag with bilberries, Bob thought how it had been a lovely holiday after all.

'I don't want to stay with Uncle Samuel and Aunt Josephine,' he had stormed when he was first told. 'I haven't seen them for years. They don't know me. Anyway, they're old, they are your uncle and aunt, not mine. There'll be nothing to do, stuck out in the country. You just want to get rid of me!'

When he had calmed down, he could see the sense of it. He couldn't go with his parents, and for one reason or another there was nowhere else for him to go. Although he tried, he couldn't convince his parents he could look after himself for three weeks. Not at thirteen, they had said.

And so he had arrived on the farm, with his dog Honey, two miles from the village with its bus once a week on market-days to Oakdale. He thought that he might never have become fond of the place if it hadn't been for 'young Kathy'.

1   What has happened, do you think, to make Bob change his mind about staying in the country?
2   Why do you think his parents say that thirteen is too young to look after yourself for three weeks?
3   What can you tell about the farm, and the people mentioned so far?
4   What can you tell about Bob's personality?
5   Why do you suppose the dog has come too?
6   What do you think will happen next?

Turn to page 13

Story 7   The Message

'Julian, come and listen to this!' shouted Dawn from her room. 'Quick!'

Julian put down the book he was reading and yawned. He was just about to get off his bed when Dawn shouted again.

'Julian, hurry, you must listen to this!'

Feeling a little irritated he got up quickly and crossed the landing to Dawn's room. She was lying down with her ear close to her cassette recorder which was on the bedside table.

'What's the urgency?' asked Julian.

'Come here and listen,' Dawn whispered. Kneeling down, Julian put his ear close to the recorder as well.

'I can't hear anything,' he said. Then, after a moment, 'Oh yes. There is a voice, but I can't make it out.'

'It's been saying something about an alarm and a galaxy, and something about the time. Just listen.'

Together they listened as hard as they could, straining their ears to catch the faint sounds.

1   Why doesn't Dawn come and ask Julian to listen?
2   Why might Julian feel irritated?
3   Why do you think Julian can't make out the voice, but Dawn can?
4   What explanations could there be for what is happening?
5   What could Julian and Dawn do to make sure they don't forget what they hear?
6   What do you think will happen next?

Turn to page 14

'Hey, Kerry,' Sam called. 'Not so deep. They said we weren't to swim.'

'This isn't deep,' Kerry called back. 'Anyway, it was no swimming they said, and stay near the edge. We're not swimming, and we're still quite near the edge.'

Sam turned away from Kerry and Susan. Kerry always went too far, often getting Susan and him into trouble. People always assumed he was the ring-leader. This time he wasn't tempted. He didn't enjoy being in deep water much. He supposed that he might enjoy it more when he learned to swim. Not that being unable to swim seemed to worry Kerry. She just loved water, deep or shallow.

Just then a scream rang out.

1   How can the girls be waist-deep yet near the edge of the water?
2   Who is most likely to get into trouble, and why?
3   Why might people assume Sam was the one who started trouble?
4   What differences in the way they behave are there between Kerry and Sam?
5   What do you know about how well each of the children can swim?
6   What do you think has happened?

Turn to page 15

'It's from the kitchen, I think,' said Peter. Indeed it was. He opened the door to find water covering the floor. It was almost level with the small step between the rooms. From the ceiling rain was dripping in three separate places.

'Surely the leaking roof couldn't cause that much of a flood?' said Michael. 'It's an inch deep. That's a lot of water.'

'It must be coming in somewhere else. We'd better find where from,' said Peter.

1   How do you account for the splash and patter?
2   Why does Michael think the leaking roof hasn't caused the flood?
3   Why did Peter think he should find out where the water is coming from?
4   How high is the step?
5   What would happen if the boys did nothing?
6   Give one thing Peter could do next.

Turn to page 16

'You don't think someone has taken it, do you?' asked Simon.

'Of course I do,' replied James. 'What else could have happened to it?'

'It must be someone who knows where you keep it,' said Simon.

'We all know that. It's a pretty obvious place, anyway,' said Neil, who had overheard the conversation. 'Have you had your bag with you all morning?'

'I don't know, let me think –'

'You didn't for games,' said Simon. 'You left it in the locker room. The calculator must have been taken then!'

'Oh yes,' said Neil. 'It must have been taken by someone who had got out of a lesson for some reason.'

1   What does Simon assume about why the thief stole the calculator?
2   Why does Simon think the calculator was taken during games?
3   What is the most practical remark made?
4   Who is putting most ideas into the discussion?
5   What reasons could someone give to get out of a lesson?
6   What do you think will happen next?

Turn to page 17

'Trust you to fall in,' said the eldest sister. 'Now we're all in trouble.'

The little girl began to cry. 'I want to go home,' she sobbed.

'You'd better stop that,' said the eldest. 'You can't go home like that. What do you think Mum will do to us when she finds out we came to the pond? She said we mustn't ever go without her. And you made me take you. You promised not to do anything silly. You're always getting me into trouble!'

'I was only reaching for a leaf,' cried the little girl. The middle sister said, 'What shall we do if we can't go home?'

'We'll take her muddy clothes off, and wash them in the water fountain, and dry them in the wind. Then we'll be able to go home.'

1   How do you suppose the younger sister made the older sister take her?
2   What do you think the mother must have said to the girls to make them so reluctant to go home?
3   Why might the mother want the girls to be afraid of her anger?
4   What do you think of the eldest sister's plan, and why?
5   What do you think the mother would say if she knew?
6   What do you think will happen next?

Turn to page 18

Joe swung his lorry to the right and drove towards the smoke. As Joe got nearer, he could hear crying and shouting. Already a small crowd had gathered round a house in the middle of the row. Now he could see flames as well as smoke coming from the burning hallway. He stopped, and saw a woman being forcibly held by two others. She kept crying, 'My children, my children are in there. I must get my children.'

Joe looked up, and caught a glimpse of choking, terrified faces at the window. Knowing the area, he could see that by the time the fire engine arrived it might be too late. Without thinking, he leaned on the horn and pushed the gear-stick into first gear.

1 Why was the woman being held forcibly?
2 Why couldn't the children get out?
3 What do you think would be the best way of getting the children out?
4 What reasons could there be for the fire engine not arriving in time to save the children?
5 Joe acts 'without thinking'. What do you think that means?
6 What do you think Joe is going to do?

Turn to page 19

'Young Kathy', as everyone seemed to call her, was a few months older than Bob. Her father was a shepherd, and she lived in a small cottage even further from the village. They had first met when Honey and he had been cornered by some fierce cows. Kathy had heard Honey barking, had come and driven the heifers away and had explained how they will often surround a dog they don't like. Honey, of course, didn't know how to behave in the country, so Kathy suggested that they took her out with Kathy's own dog, Cracker, to teach her.

They had spent a lot of time together after that, along the river-valleys, and up on the hills too. Kathy shared her knowledge and love for the place with him. She too was glad of the company, as in the holidays she usually saw no one but the younger children.

Then, on the day before he was due to go home, the accident happened.

1   Why do you think she might be referred to as 'young Kathy'?
2   Why do you suppose Bob didn't drive the cows away?
3   Why did Bob appreciate Kathy's company?
4   Why did Kathy appreciate Bob's company?
5   In what way have Bob's feelings for the countryside changed?
6   Can you guess what accident it could be?

Turn to page 20

Julian managed to hear the next words. He was just about to look for a pencil and paper to write them down, when the tape stopped. Dawn rewound it, and pressed the play button. Pop music burst into the room.

'It's disappeared,' she said. They listened until the tape ended, then tried it again. There was music again.

'How long do you reckon it lasted?' asked Julian.

'About two or three minutes, that's all,' answered Dawn.

'What do you think it was?' Julian asked. 'Was it a message?'

'I don't know,' said Dawn. 'First, let's just try to remember everything we heard and write it down.'

'Good idea,' said Julian, getting the pen and paper. 'Start right at the beginning.'

'Well, first of all I was listening to the music. Then it stopped. I thought the tape must have snapped or something, but I saw it was still turning, and so I turned up the volume. That was when I heard the voice, although it wasn't like a human voice at all.'

1   What has happened to the recording of the voice?
2   If the recording is a message, what does this imply?
3   Why does Dawn think the first thing to do is to write down what they heard?
4   What have they got to help them recall what they heard?
5   Why might the voice not sound like a human voice?
6   What do you think will happen next?

Turn to page 21

'Get her, Sam, get her!' his mother screamed from the sand dunes. For a moment Sam didn't realise what she meant. Then he looked for his sisters. Susan was crying, 'Kerry, Kerry.' Kerry was nowhere to be seen. Then her head bobbed up and her arms thrashed the water, before she went under again.

Sam knew at once Kerry was out of her depth. He realised his mother couldn't get to the water in time. He knew he was the only one who could do anything. He was terrified.

1   Why does his mother scream at Sam?
2   Why do you think Sam doesn't realise what his mother means at first?
3   Does Sam have a choice about whether to try and save Kerry?
4   How can Kerry be saved?
5   Why was Sam terrified?
6   What do you think Sam will choose to do, and why?

Turn to page 22

Peter pulled off his shoes and socks, and rolled his trouser bottoms up. He paddled across to the back door. As it opened, a gush of water splashed over his feet, wetting his trousers.

'The drain must be blocked,' he said to Michael. 'You should see how much water there is out here. It has been coming in under the door.'

Michael said, 'Hurry, the water is about to come over the step on to the carpet of this room. You'd better do something quickly.'

1 How do you know Peter wasn't prepared for what happened when he opened the back door?
2 Where did Peter find the deepest water?
3 Why should he think the drain is blocked?
4 Why is the water level getting higher?
5 What would be the consequences of a flood in the sitting room?
6 What would you do next if you were Peter, and why?

Turn to page 23

'Martin was excused games because of his ankle,' said Simon.

'And Robert had a nosebleed and had to go off,' added Neil.

Turning to Neil, Simon said, 'And you were last on the pitch because of your broken lace.'

'Are you suggesting I took the calculator?' said Neil, a flush spreading over his face.

'No, just that you could have done,' said Simon. 'I don't suppose anything can be proved against anyone. After all quite a few people have had the opportunity to take it.'

James said quietly, 'Only one person had the opportunity I've remembered. You've forgotten, we had our school photographs taken this morning. We all had to leave our bags outside. I was told someone was seen bending over my bag when I came out of the room.'

1   What is the effect on the mystery of mentioning Martin and Robert?
2   Who seems most convinced of the impossibility of finding the culprit?
3   Why do you think Neil goes red?
4   Why do you think James spoke quietly?
5   What does someone bending over James's bag suggest?
6   What do you think will happen next?

Turn to page 24

Miss Long was staying with her sister's family, and in the afternoon she and her sister had taken the youngest boy out for a walk in the park. She was pushing her nephew's pushchair as he ran ahead. In the middle of a sentence, she suddenly stopped, and said,

'What on earth are those children doing?'

Two children were running up and down, waving things in the air. The women went closer to see. As they passed a laurel bush, they heard a shaky voice call out, 'Are they dry yet? I'm freezing.'

Miss Long parted the bush. An unusual sight for a January day met her eyes.

1   What can you work out about who was in Miss Long's sister's family?
2   What do you think the children were trying to do by running about?
3   Whose was the shaky voice, and why was it coming from a bush?
4   What do you think Miss Long saw in the bush?
5   What would you do now if you were Miss Long?
6   How do you think this story will end?

Turn to page 25

He turned the lorry sharply into the path in front of the house. As soon as people realised what he was doing they got out of the way. Ploughing over the rose bushes and flower beds, Joe stopped his lorry under the window. The heat and smoke were alarming, and Joe realised he hadn't got long. He scrambled out of the passenger's window, and pulled himself up on to the cab roof. Two more men climbed on to the lorry and came after him. With a spanner in his hand, and a handkerchief round his fist, he called out to the children to stand to one side. Once the glass was broken, Joe was able to climb into the smoke-filled room, release the catch and open the window wide. He swept up the smallest girl, who was limp in her older sister's arms, and passed her out to the men on the cab. Next was the crying and coughing small boy, and lastly the older sister. Then Joe climbed back on to the cab roof himself.

1   Why hasn't Joe got long to make the rescue?
2   Why did Joe climb out of the passenger's window?
3   Why did Joe pass out the unconscious child first?
4   What has made the child lose consciousness?
5   What should be done for the child now?
6   Now what do you think will happen?

Turn to page 26

This Friday, Cracker had been left at home. At tea-time, Bob whistled for Honey. There were no answering barks. Putting down his bilberries, Bob called and searched for Honey. Kathy searched in the opposite direction. After a while, Kathy said,

'Don't worry, Bob, we'll come back after tea and look then if she hasn't come back already. She's probably still chasing rabbits.'

Honey didn't return, so after tea the friends set out again, with Cracker this time. For over an hour they searched systematically, in a circle from where she had last been seen.

'If she could hear us, she'd bark,' said Bob with conviction.

'It must mean that she's either unconscious or out of earshot,' said Kathy. 'It's funny that Cracker doesn't seem to have picked up her scent.'

'How can we find out where she is?' asked Bob. 'I've got to go home tomorrow! I can't go without her.'

Kathy said, 'We'll have to ask Dad. He's very good at finding sheep, but you'll be surprised at how he does it.'

1 What are bilberries, and what do you think Bob is going to do with them?
2 Why is it odd that Cracker hasn't picked up Honey's scent?
3 What reasons can you think of to account for Honey's disappearance?
4 Why is there a sense of urgency?
5 In what way might Kathy's father be able to help?
6 What do you think will happen next?

Turn to page 27

'The voice said something about the need for alarm. It could even have been "no need for alarm",' said Dawn. 'I just couldn't get used to the sound at first. It sounded more like a computer talking than a person.'

'Go on,' said Julian.

'I thought I must be overhearing a police message. Then I realised I couldn't be doing that, as there's no radio on this machine. Then I suddenly knew the message was for us.'

'Who?' asked Julian. 'Who's us? How do you know?'

'There was something about solar time, and some numbers, then earth time. I think the numbers were 0230 or 0320 – it definitely began with a nought. Then I heard something which sounded like "galaxy exception". I called you. I couldn't catch the next bit, then the voice said "your solar system". I thought I heard the name Pluto. Then we heard the last bit together.'

'I heard: "Our intentions are pacific".'

'That's what I thought,' said Dawn, 'But what does the Pacific have to do with it?'

1   Why did Dawn think she might be overhearing a police message?
2   What do you think makes Dawn believe the message is for them?
3   What do you think was really said instead of "galaxy exception"?
4   What is the message about?
5   Can you answer Dawn's last question?
6   What do you think will happen next?

Turn to page 28

As Sam waded into deeper water, he could feel the current tugging at his legs. He thought he was going to overbalance.

'Susan, hold my hand,' he said.

Sam found he couldn't hurry. Kerry's spluttering face had come to the surface again, but again she had gone under. Sam thought he would never be able to reach her. Fighting panic, but obedient to his mother's command, he forced himself onward. Only when he was in up to his shoulders was he able to grab one of Kerry's flailing arms and pull her towards him. She soon found her feet. Hands joined, the three of them scrambled, dripping, from the water, to be met by their breathless mother.

1   What might be the effect of the undertow on Kerry?
2   What makes Sam feel panic during the rescue?
3   What other feelings are hinted at, which Sam feels during the rescue?
4   What do you think makes Sam keep going?
5   Why is the children's mother breathless?
6   What do you think their mother would say and do now?

Peter hurried into the pouring rain. He reached where he thought the drain was. Plunging his hands into the water, he caught hold of a handful of leaves. The water started to run down the drain. He came back inside.

'That should stop more water coming in,' he said. 'But what shall we do about all this?'

'I'll have to go now,' said Michael. 'I mustn't be late, and it's nearly stopped raining. I'll go round the front way. Goodbye.'

Peter got a mop, and cloths and buckets. He mopped and squeezed for what seemed ages. He put bowls under three leaks in the roof. By the time Peter's mother came back an hour later, the sun was shining and the kitchen floor was sparkling clean. Only three bowls remained on the floor.

1 Now you know what was blocking the drain, what season do you think it is now?
2 What other reason might there be for Michael leaving?
3 Why did Michael say he would go out the front way?
4 How would you feel if you were Peter?
5 Why do you think he left bowls on the floor, even when it had stopped raining?
6 What do you think Peter's mother should do to prevent rain water coming in next time there is a rain storm?

'You were both so quick to assume the calculator went during the games lesson, but the more I thought about it, the more I felt it had gone before. I don't remember touching it when I took my games kit out,' said James.

'That's the sort of memory which can't be relied on,' said Neil. 'It's not really evidence.'

'Who was supposed to be bending over your bag?' asked Simon. 'Is that who you think the thief is? And who said so, anyway?'

'Well, that's the trouble. This person told me it was one of you two, he couldn't be sure which, in your school uniform. I don't think it will help anyone if I told you his name, because, as you said, it's not really evidence. There's only one thing I can do. I'll go for a walk, and suggest you do too, and the person who took it must put it back before the end of break.'

With that James walked off.

1   What first made James suspicious?
2   Why does Neil think that what James remembers is not good enough to be evidence?
3   Why do you suppose it wouldn't help to give the other person's name?
4   What good and bad points are there to the suggestion about the walk?
5   From what the boys have said, and how they have said it, say who you think took the calculator, showing what in the story could be used as evidence.
6   Why do you think the calculator will or will not be returned?

A small girl, dressed only in dirty, wet underclothes, stood shivering and blue with cold.

'What is happening?' demanded Miss Long, as the girls ran over. She took off her lovely white coat and wrapped it round the dirty shivering child. The girls explained.

'But she could have got pneumonia!' exclaimed Miss Long.

'I never thought of that,' said the oldest girl, sadly.

Miss Long took charge. 'We must take her home. She can go in Andrew's pushchair. I'll explain everything to your mother!'

Carrying the wet clothes, the older children followed after. They knew they were in even deeper trouble than before.

1 Why did Miss Long give the little girl her coat?
2 Why is it going to be worse for the children going home in this state, than when the girl first fell in?
3 Which of the children do you think will get into most trouble, and why?
4 How do you think the mother will feel when she sees everyone on the doorstep?
5 This adventure could have a few consequences. What might the consequence of getting involved be for Miss Long?
6 What long-term consequences might there be for each of the children?

The cab roof was scorching hot, and Joe realised he wasn't going to be able to drive his lorry away. He climbed down from the roof on to the back of the lorry, and then to the ground. He saw a woman quickly take her mouth away from the younger child's, and turn her on to her side, where she was sick. She was then wiped, and gathered into her mother's arms. The other two children had been wrapped in coats, and now all four of them were clinging together with relief. In the distance, a very welcome sound could be heard getting nearer.

Joe looked at the burning house, and at the three small children with their mother, and thought of what might have happened. That was when his courage went, and his knees started to shake. Instead of the wide awake and clear-thinking hero of a moment ago, he became ordinary Joe, hungry, thirsty, tired and ready for a bath.

1   Why couldn't Joe drive away?
2   What was happening to the youngest child?
3   Why were the others wrapped in coats?
4   What was the welcome sound?
5   When and why did Joe's courage go?
6   Joe has acted like a hero. How is he the same, or different, from other people?

Kathy's father spread out the map.

'Show me where you last saw Honey,' he said. While they watched, Kathy's father held a pendulum over the map. Slowly he moved it from place to place. Then it started to swing in an anti-clockwise direction.

'This is the place to look,' he said.

It was getting dark, so they took torches as well as spades. When he had located the area shown by the map, Kathy's father started walking slowly to and fro with two rods held loosely in his hands. At the point where the rods suddenly swung towards each other, crossing as they went, he stopped.

'I think Honey's here somewhere,' he said. Bob whistled. There was silence, then a faint whimper could be heard. Very carefully, they started digging. Kathy's father said, 'I think there's been a tunnel here. I reckon she's gone after a rabbit.'

Then there was a glimpse of golden fur, and Honey was lifted out of the earth, trembling, weak, dirty, but with a tail wagging feebly.

'Thank you,' said Bob. 'She owes her life to you. But how did you know where to find her?'

1   What does Kathy's father find out with the map?
2   How does the pendulum tell him where to go?
3   What does Kathy's father do with the rods, and how?
4   Why is Honey trembling?
5   What is the most likely explanation for Honey getting stuck?
6   What is the most likely explanation for Honey being found?

'Pacific means peaceful,' said Julian. 'This sounds like a warning message. It sounds as if there is going to be an inspection of our solar system in our galaxy. If it is peaceful, then it probably was "no cause for alarm" you heard.'

'The numbers must mean when the inspection takes place,' said Dawn. 'I wish I could have written them down at the time.'

'I'll just look in the paper,' said Julian. He went to get it. 'No, there's nothing on the radio or television we could have heard. Do you think we could have had a message from space?'

'What else could it be?' said Dawn. 'What shall we do about it?'

'Nothing,' said Julian. 'We've got no evidence. Everyone will think it's a joke if we say anything. And even if it is true, then there is no cause for alarm.'

Next morning at breakfast, their mother said,

'Look at the paper! While you two were having sweet dreams, they say a UFO was sighted over Crowhall Common. It's amazing what some people will believe!'

1   Whom do you think the message is aimed at?
2   Whom do you think the message is from?
3   What is the purpose of the message?
4   Do you think Julian and Dawn were right not to say anything?
5   What time do you think the UFO was sighted?
6   Why is the mother amazed at what some people believe?

Story 8   Alligator Nightmare

The alligators twisted their bodies and snapped their jaws as they slithered round each other. Over and under they went, biting and snorting as they rolled about. The water bubbled and foamed as it was beaten by the smack of powerful tails. It became more and more muddy as it was churned up. The wash made by their heavy bodies as the alligators surged through the water almost knocked me under, loosening my grasp on a root sticking out from the steep and slippery bank. Regaining my balance, I clung to the root even harder. I was grateful for the noise and movement which had so far concealed my presence in the water, but knew I could not remain where I was for much longer without being discovered. The thought of discovery was chilling. I tried to control my mind. A decision was needed. I would have to do something.

1   How do you know where the story is set?
2   What are the alligators doing?
3   What do you think the storyteller is doing in the water?
4   What dangers is the storyteller in?
5   Why has the storyteller been lucky so far?
6   What do you think will happen next?

Turn to page 33

Story 9   Voice from the Past

Grandmother was very strait-laced. She wasn't at all like the fairy-tale Grannies you read of in books. She never laughed, and I rarely saw her smile. She was kind to me, but never seemed very interested in what I did. When we went for tea, she sat upright on a straight-backed chair. I used to feel nervous about crumbs and spills. I always felt that she was rather like the furniture in her rather dark house – very old fashioned and respectable, dark and gloomy, and built to last. Both the furniture and Grandmother made me feel small and cramped, as if I couldn't be me in her house.

My ideas about Grandmother underwent a drastic change when I was about twelve. That was when her old friend, May Cooper, came to stay with her.

1   What can you tell about fairy-tale Grannies from this passage?
2   Why might the Grandmother choose a straight-backed chair?
3   Why did the child feel nervous when visiting?
4   Why should the child feel small and cramped in Grandmother's house?
5   What do you think May Cooper will have to do with the story?
6   What do you think will happen next?

Turn to page 34

Story 10 **The Skull**

Tim walked casually down the garden, the skull held carelessly under his arm. His father was at the kitchen window, looking absent-mindedly down the garden towards the church. Tim knew that if he hurried, or even looked more cheerful than usual, he might be noticed. He had found out long ago that an almost blank expression, and a fairly aimless manner, were the best to use if adult attention was not to be aroused. Haste or stealth always seemed to put his parents on the alert straight away.

So it was that Tim's father finished the dishes, noticing only that Tim had come in. Tim was able to carry his treasure up to his room quite openly. It was lucky his four-year-old sister was not around, as she was too shrewd to be put off by appearances. She would have noticed his unusual load immediately. Not the slightest change in him escaped her notice, and she would pursue him tirelessly, asking questions. He sometimes felt like screaming when she persisted, but didn't. He knew she was just terribly interested in him, and every little thing he did. Anyway, he didn't have Louise to face, so Tim was able to go into his room, shut the door, and put his prize carefully down on the table.

1 Why should hurrying alert Tim's parents?
2 Why does Tim not want his father to notice him?
3 What do you know about how Tim feels about the skull, and how do you know it?
4 What can you tell about the relationship between Tim and Louise?
5 Why does Tim carry the skull carelessly and put it down carefully?
6 How and where could Tim have got the skull?

Turn to page 35

Story 11 The Ring

1881 was a year of rejoicing for James Claypole and Emma Sewell, for that was the year they got married. The Claypoles grew wealthy. More tiles than ever were produced. Only one area of their lives was a disappointment, and this was the fact that Emma produced only daughters. After six girls, James and Emma were resigned to not having their long-desired son. Great was their delight when the seventh child proved to be a boy. As a token of his pleasure, James bought Emma a very beautiful pearl and ruby ring. The boy was christened Francis, and brought up as heir to the business.

Before Emma died, she gave the ring to Francis. She said she wanted it kept in the family. He was to give the ring to his future wife when he decided to marry.

Francis worked hard at the business. Little did James Claypole realise that Elizabeth Dawson was the main reason for the long hours. She helped with the book-keeping, and Francis was in love with her, and she with him.

The match was plainly impossible. She was the daughter of a bricklayer, who had made the most of the education which had come her way. Not being able to face the idea of life without her, Francis resolved to speak to his father.

1   What can you tell about the Claypole business?
2   Why should daughters be considered a disappointment?
3   Why did James give such a lovely ring to Emma?
4   After Francis's wife, who should receive the ring?
5   What is Francis going to speak about?
6   What do you think James Claypole will say and do?

Turn to page 36

As sensibly as I could, I considered my position. If I tried to climb up the bank, I would surely be seen. A swipe with a tail or a pair of long jaws would soon have me back in the water. I didn't like to dwell on what would happen then ... Anyway, I most probably wouldn't make it up the bank, because of its steepness. Looking up, I could see nothing I could use as hand holds. The earth of the bank was wet and slippery from the splashing. There seemed to be no roots higher up. On the other hand, if I stayed where I was, sooner or later the alligators would detect me. There was really no chance that they would just swim away. This was their stretch of river. I couldn't decide. Both courses of action seemed impossible and hopeless, my mind seemed frozen. Then, another awful thought came to me which at least helped me decide what to do. What else might there be lurking in these infested waters?

1   Why is going up the bank not a very good idea?
2   Why is staying in the same place not a very good idea?
3   What does the storyteller not want to think about?
4   What would you choose to do?
5   What awful thought do you think the writer has had?
6   What do you think will happen next?

Turn to page 37

The day I overheard Grandmother giggling – yes, giggling – I realised there was more to her than I had ever guessed. For the first time I was curious. I resolved to ask my mother about her childhood when I got a chance.

'Grandmother laughed today,' I said. 'I've never heard her laugh before. She sounded so young. She's always seemed so old and sad to me.'

'I suppose you only know her as an old woman,' my mother said. 'She's aged a lot since your Grandfather died. What a pity you can't remember him. He was devoted to her.'

'He wasn't your real father, though, was he?'

'No, but I always wished he had been. I would have liked a father like him,' said my mother sadly.

'What happened to your real father?' I asked.

'I don't know. Your grandmother never talked about it. I gather he died after I was born. Mother must have married again, but I don't know how long after. My earliest memories include them both. I always called him Father.'

1   What effect did the giggling have on the child?
2   What do you know about when the two Grandfathers died?
3   Why would the mother wish the stepfather had been her real father?
4   Why might the Grandmother not want to talk about her first marriage?
5   What can you tell about what the Grandmother and her second husband felt about each other?
6   What do you think will happen next?

Turn to page 38

Tim's skull was complete. Even the teeth were still in the jaw. Tim wondered how old it was. He didn't know how he could find out. He couldn't believe his luck. He must have been the first person to walk along the churchyard path since the tree blew down in the storm. He had seen the glimpse of white amongst the stones and soil between the roots, and simple excavation with his hands had revealed the skull. He assumed there was probably the rest of the skeleton in there too, but it was still buried under the tree.

It was a beautiful skull, though a little on the small side. Perhaps it was a child's skull? He looked again at the teeth. There were twenty-four. They were all fairly small. He looked in the mirror at his own teeth. He had twenty-four too, but his front teeth were larger. Now he was sure it was a child's skull, and that it had probably belonged to a child of not more than six. He wondered about the owner, and why he or she had died so young. For the first time he felt a twinge of doubt about the wisdom of bringing the skull home. 'I won't keep it,' he promised himself. 'I'll put it back soon.'

1   What reasons could there be for not bringing a skull into the house?
2   What can you tell about how long the skull had been buried?
3   Tim and the skull have the same number of teeth. Why are Tim's larger?
4   Why does Tim think the owner of the skull was not more than six?
5   What is there to show how Tim feels about his decision to bring home the skull?
6   What do you think will happen next?

Turn to page 39

James Claypole was shocked and furious. As far as he was concerned, any marriage between Francis and Elizabeth Dawson was unthinkable. He refused to allow his son to see her again. Disobedience, he threatened, would result in Francis being disinherited and being turned out of the house without a penny.

Francis was devastated. He thought carefully of his prospects, the factory, the big house, the servants, the wealth, and the safe future. He thought of Elizabeth. It didn't take him long to make up his mind. His father, true to his word, never gave him another penny. He lived the rest of his life as though he had never had a son.

He never knew of the life Francis tried to build for himself and Elizabeth. He never knew of the twins born to Elizabeth, who had both died, or of the son who lived. He never knew of Elizabeth's illness which seemed to be weakening her day by day. He never knew how hard Francis worked to try to pay for the food and medicine Elizabeth so desperately needed. And when the doctor told Francis that Elizabeth's only hope was to go away to the country for a few months, James Claypole never knew of Francis's struggle with his conscience, which resulted in him entering a small shop over which was the sign *Jewellery Bought and Sold*.

1   What makes James Claypole think Francis will do as he is told?
2   Why is James Claypole shocked and furious?
3   In the light of what happened to Francis, do you think he made the right decision, and why?
4   What does Francis intend to do?
5   What was Francis struggling with his conscience about?
6   What do you think will happen next?

Turn to page 40

All sorts of memories came floating into my mind. I thought of all those travel and adventure stories I'd read, set in South America. I remembered the plight of a girl whose plane had crashed in the jungle. I thought of the hazards she had faced. It suddenly all came back to me. Was it here where there were those vicious shoals of fish? I remembered the details. The fish were piranha fish, and they were carnivorous. Any animal unfortunate enough to fall in the water would have its bones picked clean of all its flesh in less than a minute. And the fish didn't mind which species the next meal belonged to ... I was sure I'd read they lived in the same rivers as alligators. As these thoughts flashed through my mind and I was just imagining what it would feel like to be eaten alive, there was a tingling and nibbling around my leg.

1   What do you think has triggered off these thoughts?
2   What new consequences could there be if the storyteller stayed in the water?
3   What facts does the storyteller remember?
4   What thoughts and what feelings do you think the storyteller is putting together?
5   What reasons could there be for the tingling feeling?
6   What do you think will happen next?

Turn to page 43

Grandmother and May Cooper came to tea the next day. May was a bright, lively, chatty sort of woman. She wore a red skirt and a yellow cardigan. Her lips were orange, her eye-lids blue and her hair an unnatural reddish-brown. Seeing May next to Grandmother, who was in her dark wool suit, I wondered what on earth they had in common.

'Have you and Grandmother been friends for a long time?' I asked May.

'Dearie me, yes,' laughed May. 'We worked the theatres together.'

'Theatres?' I couldn't believe it. Grandmother on the stage? Perhaps she had been a serious actress – or a wardrobe mistress. Yes, that was more like it.

'We were in the chorus line together!' May chuckled. 'Do you recall those feathers, Agnes? Do you remember when we were appearing in Newcastle? –' and May collapsed in laughter. To my surprise, Grandmother joined in. Then she said,

'Let's not let too many secrets out of the bag, May!'

1   What do May's clothes and appearance say about her?
2   What effect does May have on Grandmother?
3   What have May and Grandmother got in common?
4   Why does the child imagine Grandmother as a wardrobe mistress?
5   What did the Grandmother really do?
6   What is there in the passage to suggest what may happen next?

Turn to page 44

Tim heard voices downstairs. As quickly as he could, he put the skull on an old tin plate and lowered it into a cardboard box. This he put in the bottom of his wardrobe. He draped his dressing-gown and old jeans over it, to look as if they had just slipped off their hangers.

There were footsteps on the stairs. The handle of the door started to turn, then returned to its original position. It turned again, and then again. He knew it was Louise, who couldn't quite turn the handle far enough.

'Open the door, Tim,' she called.

Tim opened the door and she fell in. Picking herself up, she said,

'What are you doing?'

'Nothing,' replied Tim. 'Where have you been?'

'To a party,' said Louise. 'I had ice cream. There was a cake with pink on the top. How long is it to my birthday?'

'A long time,' said Tim. 'It's my birthday next, then yours.'

'We played hiding,' said Louise. 'Can I play hiding in your cupboard, and you find me?'

'No,' Tim said quickly, 'we'll play it downstairs.'

1   Why do you think Tim put the skull on a plate?
2   Why did Tim arrange the clothes the way he did?
3   Why do you think Tim didn't want anyone to find the skull?
4   Why did Louise fall into Tim's bedroom?
5   Why did Tim suggest playing hide-and-seek downstairs?
6   What do you think will happen next?

Turn to page 45

Bill Mason had finished working down the pit. It would only be a matter of time before he was in France, fighting for his country. He was impatient to go, eager to play his part, to be seen to be a man. Perhaps now he was going, Grace would think differently of him, he thought.

He had been courting Grace for four months, but whenever he turned the talk to the future, she wouldn't join in.

'Why think about tomorrow?' she'd say. 'Who can say what will happen to any of us?'

Bill didn't like to go away with nothing arranged.

Now, on his last weekend at home, Bill caught sight of a beautiful pearl and ruby ring in a jeweller's window. Grace would never be able to resist it, he thought, and they would be engaged. He decided to throw caution to the winds, and returned with all his savings. He never understood Grace's reaction. With tears in her eyes she refused to take it.

On the train going away, Bill felt angry and hurt by turns. She hadn't agreed to wait for him, though she hadn't refused to see him when he came home on leave. In the meanwhile here he was with no money, no girl, and a stupid ring. Not caring any more, he wound down the window and reached into his pocket.

1   What is Bill going to do after this weekend?
2   What does Bill want Grace to think about him?
3   What is Grace's attitude to the future?
4   Why does Bill buy the ring?
5   Why do you think Grace refuses to have Bill's ring?
6   What is Bill going to do?

Turn to page 46

Story 12   Anne's Diary

2nd September 1731

Today, a most strange thing happened. About mid-day, what appeared to be a wild animal of some sort appeared in the village. This 'thing' was first seen rooting about amongst the long grasses of the churchyard, at the edge of the village. It was seen by my younger brother, Georges, and two of his friends. They crept stealthily through the grass and between the gravestones for a closer look. At first they thought it had four legs, but then they realised it had two legs and two arms, because it was putting something into its mouth with a sort of hand, and making crunching and grunting noises. Georges said their hearts almost stopped beating when this animal stood up on its hind legs, alert, and looked straight towards them. They froze. They could see it wasn't large, but it seemed familiar and yet quite strange. They knew then this was no ordinary animal.

1   What can you tell about the setting for this story?
2   Where do you think this creature has come from?
3   Why did the boys go for a closer look?
4   What was the creature doing?
5   What effect did the creature have on the boys?
6   What do you think the creature might be?

Turn to page 42

2nd September 1731 continued

The creature moved off, not, apparently, having seen them. Georges and his friends came back to tell my father, who is the blacksmith in our village. My father and older brother Jacques, and Jean and Marc from the next house, went out with sticks and straps to capture this wild thing. Georges kept insisting it was like a human being, a wild boy of some sort.

After a while, the men came back. Between them they were carrying a twisting, writhing shape, bound with leather thongs. It was screaming and hissing and shouting. No words could be made out, just frightful yowls. A crowd of on-lookers gathered, and there was talking and muttering. No one could decide what to do. Eventually they decided to put the creature in the stable belonging to the priest until Father Paul came home that night. As the struggling thing was untied, we could see that it was a human of some sort, filthy, with long matted hair, and lightly covered with animal skins. Fighting fiercely all the time, it was locked in the stable, from which came the most violent thumps as it tried to break down the door.

1 Why do you think the creature was captured?
2 Why were sticks and straps considered necessary?
3 What can you tell about the creature's abilities?
4 What can you tell about the creature's state of mind?
5 What problems were solved by locking it in the stable?
6 What do you think will happen next?

Turn to page 47

There wasn't a choice any more. I decided I had to leave the water some-how. I looked around carefully. With my heart in my mouth I inched my way downstream for some yards, very slowly, going from root to root. As I went, I had plenty of time to search the bank with my eyes, looking for any likely hand and foot holds. After what seemed miles, though it was not many yards further down river, I saw a section of bank which looked as if it might be just about possible to climb. I decided to take the risk. Once I'd made my decision, with a great deal of difficulty I pulled myself clear of the water, by means of roots and depressions in the steep bank. With water running from me, I clutched the bank, keeping as still as I could be. The alligators played on. For the first time I dared to look down at my leg. It was still whole, but with disgust and horror I could see the reason for the tingling.

1   Why did the storyteller go downstream rather than upstream?
2   What does the storyteller say in the passage which is not literally true, what does it mean, and why choose to say it this way?
3   Why did the storyteller move slowly?
4   Why is it difficult to leave the water?
5   Why do you think the storyteller waited so long to look at the leg?
6   What do you think would be the reason for the tingling?

Turn to page 49

'Was Grandmother trying to keep May quiet, do you think?' I asked Mother later. 'I didn't know she worked in the theatre. When was that?'

'It was before she was married. I don't ever remember her talking about it to us. I just picked things up from the odd thing May said, and from Father. I gather she was the youngest of ten children. Her parents were well off, but distant and remote. They had a nanny and servants to look after them. When she was only four, her mother died, and her father soon after. From then on she was passed round the family from brother to sister like a parcel. I gather they treated her like an unpaid servant, she had to scrub and clean and look after her nieces and nephews, and never knew anything she could call home. When she was eighteen she ran away, and somehow or other went on the stage. I believe she sent a photo back to the oldest brother after six months, of herself dressed as a chorus girl. The brother was shocked, and wrote and told her the family never wanted to see her as long as she lived. She had let down the family name.'

1   Why do you think the Grandmother may not have talked about her life in the theatre?
2   Where did the Grandmother live after her parents died?
3   Why did she run away?
4   Why do you suppose she sent a photograph to her oldest brother?
5   What can you tell about what some people thought of going on the stage?
6   What can you tell about Grandmother's character from this passage?

Turn to page 50

When Tim went up to bed, he was just about to go to sleep when he heard Louise cry out. He hurried in to her room. She was crying and kept saying that her head hurt. By this time her parents had come up.

'What's the matter with her?' asked Tim.

'I don't know,' said his mother. 'She's very hot. She's obviously got a headache. It's hard to know at this stage. There aren't any spots.'

'Probably something she ate at the party,' said his father. 'Anyway, you go to bed, Tim.'

Tim went back to bed. His father went downstairs. His mother stayed with Louise. He was worried. He had never seen her like this. She had seemed not to recognise him. She was so rarely ill. Even when she had chicken-pox she hadn't seemed as ill as this. He thought of the owner of the skull. He, or she, wouldn't have been much older than Louise. How had that child died? Perhaps it had started with an illness like Louise's? He shuddered. Now he was being ridiculous. Louise wasn't that ill. His father thought it was only something she'd eaten. Then he heard his mother calling, 'Michael, Michael!' His father came running up the stairs, two at a time.

'Phone the doctor,' said his mother. 'She's getting worse.'

1   What makes Tim so worried?
2   What effect does thinking of the skull have on Tim?
3   How does he try to reassure himself?
4   What is Tim afraid of?
5   What does the mother want the doctor for?
6   What do you think will happen next?

Turn to page 51

Robin and Beryl were out walking together. It was very warm and Robin felt hot in his uniform.

'Let's sit down in that shade by the railway line,' said Beryl.

They climbed over the fence, and sat under the trees on the bank which sloped gently down to the track.

'There's something sharp here,' said Robin. Digging in the grass with his fingers, he picked up a ring, dirty with soil. He spat on his handkerchief and rubbed the ring.

'This is beautiful,' he said. 'I want to give it to you, Beryl. I couldn't afford anything as lovely as this. Will you marry me after the war? Will you wear this ring for me?'

'Oh yes,' said Beryl, 'I'll wear it always. And I'll wait for ever for you. But do you think I should have it? Someone might be looking for it.'

'How could we find where it came from? It's a gift from Heaven, meant for you.'

After Robin returned to the war, he and Beryl wrote often. Then, letters from Robin stopped coming, and it was only a matter of time before Beryl received the official letter.

She still wore the ring, except when she was doing any work which might have damaged it, which was how it came to be on the kitchen windowsill of the farm, some years later, when William Brown came looking for a job.

1   Why is a railway cutting an odd place to find a ring?
2   Do you think Robin is right to give Beryl the ring?
3   What happens to Robin?
4   What happens to Beryl?
5   Why does Beryl keep on wearing the ring?
6   What do you think William Brown will have to do with the story?

Turn to page 52

3rd September 1731

Last night the villagers met together. My father said there was talk of letting the wild thing go. But others said, if it was a human being, it had a human soul, and should be saved. The priest, Father Paul, is to be responsible. They are to prepare a better place for the creature. My father worked on the bars all today, and has fitted them to the front of a stone pig house so that the wild thing can get fresh air and light, and food can be given through the bars. I have not seen the wild thing today, although we have all heard it. Water was taken to the stable by Father Paul, but the creature knocked him down, and scratched and bit Marc and Jacques as they prevented it from escaping. It seems no calmer today. Perhaps by tomorrow it will be quieter, and may receive food. We have all prayed for its soul. I wonder what it feels like, to be in a strange dark place on your own.

Where has it come from? Why does it want to get away?

1   Why did the villagers meet?
2   Why is Father Paul made responsible?
3   How and why does Anne's father work to help the creature?
4   Why do you think the creature attacked the people who brought water?
5   How does Anne feel about the creature?
6   What do you think the creature will do next?

Turn to page 48

4th September 1731

Today the creature was moved to the new place. All the village came to watch. The biggest surprise is that it is female. It seems to be a girl, my mother says a bit younger than me, so it will be about ten years old. How can a girl be so wild, and so strong? I suppose I must call it 'she' from now on, although it seems scarcely human. She fought like a wild cat today, and is still refusing food and water. My father says that she can't go on like this much longer. Father Paul says he has heard of cases like this before. In 1719, Monsieur Rousseau saw two wild boys in the Pyrenees. They were running about like wild goats. And in the forest lands there are many stories of bear-children. Sometimes the children learn to live on their own, sometimes other animals adopt them. I wonder what happened to our wild girl? She can't speak. She doesn't know we mean her no harm. We all want to help. I wish she could learn to trust us. We are all praying for her.

1   Why is Anne surprised the creature is a wild girl?
2   How is the wild girl reacting to her treatment?
3   Why is the father so sure she won't carry on refusing food and water?
4   What is the effect on Anne of thinking of the creature as 'she'?
5   How do you think a child might become wild in the first place?
6   How do you think the wild girl will react to continued caging?

Turn to page 53

It was not easy to pick the swollen leeches from my leg. I didn't like the feel of them, and they clung. My blood ran freely from where they had bitten me. I hoped the alligators couldn't smell it. After this distasteful operation, I slowly heaved myself higher up the bank. The alligators splashed on, still unaware of me and my whereabouts. Now I was well clear of the water. Against all my instincts I moved, slowly, so slowly, up the bank, trying to spread my weight. Then the terrible thing happened. As I reached for a handhold, without warning a root snapped under my foot. Unable to save myself, I slipped downwards, my other holds breaking with the sudden shift in weight. I could hear my own splash as I hit the water. When I surfaced, I shook my head like a dog, and looked towards the alligators. I was at once aware, even through blurred eyes, that they had halted their play. They were looking in my direction.

1 Why was it not easy to remove the leeches?
2 Why should removing the leeches be distasteful?
3 Why was it against the storyteller's instinct to move slowly?
4 Why are the storyteller's eyes blurred?
5 Why do you think it might be important to the story that the alligators stop playing?
6 How could this story end?

Turn to page 55

'What a sad story,' I said. 'Did she never see any of her family again?'

'No, I don't think so,' said my mother. 'I remember when I was small, being sent to the country. I had been ill, and my mother was told I wouldn't get better if I didn't get out of the city, so she swallowed her pride and wrote and asked if I could stay with them. I stayed in the lodge with the gamekeeper and his wife, and only dimly remember the big house, which of course I only saw from a distance. I don't even know where it was.'

The next day, early in the morning, we got a phone call from May. Grandmother had died in her sleep.

After the funeral, I heard May ask my mother if she could talk to her. They went off up to the guest room where May had been staying. When she reappeared, my mother's eyes were red, but she seemed happier. I couldn't understand it.

1   Why does the child think the story is sad?
2   What can you tell about the Grandmother's feeling for her daughter?
3   What thoughts do you think Grandmother would have had when she wrote to her family?
4   Why did the daughter stay in the lodge?
5   What effect does the conversation with May have on the mother?
6   What do you think May can have said?

Turn to page 56

In twenty minutes the doctor arrived. Tim's father showed him up to the big bedroom, where they had taken Louise. Tim strained his ears to try and catch what the doctor and his parents were speaking about. Then there were footsteps going downstairs again. His father came back up and popped his head round Tim's door.

'What did he say?' asked Tim. 'Is Louise going to be all right?'

'Well,' said his father, 'if she gets worse she'll have to go to hospital.'

'What did the doctor say was the matter?' asked Tim nervously. 'Is it measles or anything like that?'

'That's the funny thing,' said his father. 'The doctor didn't know. He said it was probably a mystery virus and he couldn't do anything except try to bring her temperature down. We're to get in touch again if she isn't better by the morning. Anyway, try not to worry about it, and get some sleep yourself.'

Again Tim lay in bed trying to go to sleep. He was even more worried. His father hadn't said Louise would get better. The doctor didn't know what was the matter. After what seemed ages he heard his parents go to bed. The house became quiet. For the moment, everyone appeared to be sleeping.

Tim got out of bed, drew his curtains back, and by the light of the moon, put his clothes on over his pyjamas.

1   What does 'strain his ears' mean, and why does Tim do it?
2   Why does the doctor want to bring Louise's temperature down, and how can it be done?
3   What is really worrying Tim?
4   Why does Tim dress by moonlight?
5   What do you think Tim is going to do?
6   How do you think this story will end?

Turn to page 57

William Brown was desperate for work. He had been unemployed since he last came out of hospital. He knew he was lucky not to have died, yet when he was breathless and ill, fighting for every painful breath through the broken spongy mess which was left of his lungs, he wished he had done. He knew his lungs would never recover from the damage done by the mustard gas. Sometimes months would go by between painful bouts of illness, and in these William tried to work. But it was now 1926, and work was short even for healthy men. And so, when his eyes alighted on the ring by the open window, the temptation proved too great.

In a flash he reached through and put the ring in his pocket. He started to walk the five miles back to the town and his sister's house. He decided he would sell the ring. It would help to tide them all over the misery of being poor and hungry for a little while.

By the time he reached the house he was feeling feverish and ill. He decided to lie down straight away and as he removed his clothes he heard something fall. He groped round on the floor, but couldn't find the ring. By this time William felt so bad, he crawled into bed. He could look in the morning.

1   Where and how was William injured?
2   After coming out of hospital, what sort of life has William got to look forward to?
3   How would you defend William's action in stealing the ring?
4   Why do you think William couldn't find the ring?
5   What do you think will happen to William?
6   What do you think will happen to the ring?

Turn to page 58

5th September 1731

We have decided to call her Roma. This is because of the story of Romulus and Remus. They were the twins who founded Rome, and they were wild children brought up by a she-wolf. Today, Roma is quieter. She still will not eat, but has drunk water. Some of the smaller children poke her with sticks, and throw stones. Then she screams and shouts in a blind rage. After that she goes quiet in a corner, as if she doesn't want to live.

6th September 1731

My mother has tried giving her fruit and bread but Roma won't have them. My father suggested giving her raw meat, but she still won't have it. She only drinks water. Father Paul has put a stop to the sticks and stones.

7th September 1731

My brothers had a good idea. They went hunting in the churchyard where they saw Roma eating. They brought back the roots of couch grass, snails, a vole, a mouse, a frog, worms and beetles. They were put in a covered box in her cage. She took off the lid, the frog jumped out, but quick as a flash, she caught it and ate it. She did the same with the mouse and vole, but rejected the rest. My brothers were kept busy for the rest of the day fetching frogs and catching mice.

1 Why was the wild girl named, and why Roma?
2 Why has she drunk water?
3 Why did the father suggest raw meat?
4 Why does Roma eat frogs and mice?
5 What can you tell about Roma's state of mind now?
6 How do you see Roma living from now on?

Turn to page 54

14th September 1731

We have discovered Roma will also eat raw fish. My brothers have been in charge of collecting food for her. Father Paul has been giving her the food, and sitting near her while she eats it. She is quieter now, and has stopped attacking people. I think she is getting used to us. Father Paul has been trying to teach her her name. It is very important that she learns to speak, or how else can she learn of Jesus and her immortal soul? Sometimes I go and talk to her through the bars. I think perhaps she will not be so afraid of me, being a girl myself, and not so much older. Her eyes are so sad. She looks trapped. I think perhaps I should creep down at night and let her go, but then I think of what Father Paul says, and I don't. He says she is lucky, that we will save her from her animal nature. I wish she could understand that.

1   Why might eating raw fish be considered an improvement?
2   How is Roma changing?
3   How is Anne changing?
4   Do you think Roma is lucky? Give reasons.
5   What is Anne tempted to do, and why?
6   What do you think the situation will be in two years?

Turn to page 59

I realised then that a superhuman effort was required if I wanted to save myself. As I sometimes do in tight spots like this, I breathed deeply, summoning all the resources I could muster. First my shoulders moved, then my elbows, then my whole arms were involved in the strong muscular actions. At first the effort was colossal, and I began to think I no longer had the strength to lift my own weight. When I was on the point of giving up and submitting to my fate, at last I rose from the water, gaining height second by second. The alligators reached the place where I had been a moment before and snapped at me, but I was able to draw my feet up in time and was soon out of their reach. Flying strongly now, my last sight was of the river far below me. I expect you can guess where I found myself next!

1   What effort is needed to get out of the situation?
2   How does the storyteller know what to do?
3   What was the point of moving the shoulders and elbows?
4   What is different between this and previous escapes?
5   Where do you suppose the storyteller ended up next?
6   Where in the story, and why, do you realise how the story is going to end?

'I learnt something that made me happy and sad today,' Mother said later. 'I learnt that my step-father was my real Father. The man I always wished was my Father, but felt I had no right to call him that, really did belong to me.'

'But why was it a secret?' I asked.

'Because my Mother and Father weren't married when I was born,' said my mother. 'Apparently my Father, who was a lot older than my Mother, was already married.'

'But where was his wife?' I asked, confused.

'In what they called a lunatic asylum. She'd been there for twenty years before my parents met. May says my Mother and Father fell in love and set up house together. That was a scandal in those days. Then I was born. When Father's wife died soon after, he married Mother.'

'Did her awful family know?'

'Yes, her next sister said she would visit her, but only after dark. Grandmother told her not to bother.'

'But why weren't you told?' I asked.

'May says it was because Father wanted to protect Mother. He told May to tell me only after your Grandmother had died. He said to tell me he would have been proud for the world to know I was his daughter. And he hoped I'd understand.'

I don't know if Mother did. I didn't.

1   What does the Mother find sad about the news?
2   What was the matter with Grandfather's first wife?
3   What was considered a scandal, and why do you think this was?
4   Why did the sister offer to visit the Grandmother only at night?
5   Do you think keeping the secret was the kindest thing to do for all concerned?
6   This story could have ended differently, and the secret been kept. How?

Tim opened the wardrobe door and carefully lifted out the box. He carried it downstairs with only a slight rattle that fortunately didn't disturb anyone. He crept through the house to the back door, changed his slippers for his wellington boots, unlocked the door and crept into the night. In a few minutes he came to the churchyard. It looked very different by moonlight, with sharp black shadows. He hurried to where the tree had gone over. He climbed into the hole, and as far as he was able he replaced the skull where he had found it. Then he covered it over with earth. Relieved, he climbed out of the hole, wiping over his footsteps as he went. He pick up the box and plate, and, ripping up the box, put them in the rubbish bin nearby. As quietly as he had left, he returned, locked up, washed his dirty hands, and went to bed.

For the third time that night he lay trying to go to sleep. He had done all he could. He had returned the skull. He hoped it would be enough. The last thing he remembered was the church clock striking one.

His mother woke him for school.

'How's Louise?' he asked.

'Much better this morning,' said his mother. 'I nearly sent for the doctor again, her breathing was so odd and she was saying such odd things. And then, about a quarter to one, she sighed and started to breathe peacefully again. Her temperature is down and she is fine now.'

1   What would have caused the slight rattle?
2   Why are the shadows sharp and black?
3   Why did Tim dispose of the box and plate?
4   Why is Tim relieved?
5   Why did Tim return the skull?
6   Do you think there is a connection between the skull and Louise's illness?

For William, morning never came.

In time, his sister and family left the house, and tenants came and went. Because of the damage done during the Second World War, the house was abandoned, derelict and dangerous. It took many years after the war for the waste areas to be cleared and built on again. For parents living nearby, these wastelands were a nightmare, while for the children they were a dream.

In the early 1950s, a group of children were playing on this still uncleared site. It was Lizzie's turn to be 'it'. The others scattered. Frank climbed up a staircase to the remains of a bedroom. There was a hole in the floor, and part of the supporting wall below was missing. Crawling to the far corner on all fours, with his head low, he caught a glint of something, between the floor of the bedroom and the ceiling of the room below. Stretching out his arm, he was just able to reach it. It was a beautiful ring.

He was waiting in the hall when Lizzie came looking. He showed her what he had found.

'What a beauty,' she said. 'What are you going to do with it then, Frank Claypole?'

'I'm going to keep it,' Frank replied. 'It's our secret, Lizzie. Maybe one day I'll give it to you.'

1   Why didn't William recover the ring?
2   How was the house damaged?
3   How can a dream place for the children be a nightmare for the parents?
4   Why did Frank cross the floor as he did?
5   What does Frank mean about giving the ring to Lizzie?
6   Who are Frank and Lizzie?

2nd September 1733

It is now two years since we found Roma. Father Paul's patience is beginning to bear fruit. Roma can recognise a few words, and makes a sound like 'Oh Ma', pointing at herself. She can put her hands together, and bow her head when she hears the name of Jesus. Thanks to my mother, whom she has learned to trust, Roma can wash and dress herself in decent clothes, and she will now eat some of our cooked food. We are trying to keep her from eating raw food like an animal. However, she still tries to escape and we have to keep her locked up, but now she is in a room in our house. Father Paul gives her lessons and reads from the Bible to her every day. Apart from when she tries to escape, and that is when someone forgets to lock the door, she is very quiet, and I think still sad. She has been ill several times in the last few months, which seems odd to me when I think of the physical hardships she must have suffered before we found her. Or did she suffer? I wonder if she was happy as she was. Could a human being be happy as an animal?

1   In what ways is Roma more like a human and less like an animal?
2   How far is Father Paul succeeding in his aims?
3   Why do you think Roma has been ill so often?
4   What can you tell about Roma's state of mind?
5   Do you think she is better or worse off than when she was wild, and why?
6   How do you think this story will end?

Turn to page 60

14th June 1743

It is nearly ten years since I abandoned this diary. Before I put it away for ever, I must finish Roma's story. Soon my baby will be born and I must prepare our cottage. Perhaps my child will one day read Roma's story and understand it better than I.

Roma entered a convent nearly two years ago. There she took part in the daily life as much as she was able. Her language and understanding had increased, but she never could talk about her life before she was with us. She seemed to have no memory of those first ten years. To grow up with no knowledge of your own kind, or even of a mother seems so terrible to me. How did she come to be on her own and abandoned?

Today I heard that Roma has died. Her short, only half-remembered life is over. I can only comfort myself with the knowledge that she did come to know something of what it is like to be human. She did come to know God.

1   Why might Anne have stopped filling in the diary?
2   Why might Anne want to finish the story now?
3   Why do you think Roma could not talk about her years in the wild?
4   Why do you suppose Roma entered the convent?
5   What might have happened to Roma if she'd never been caught?
6   How do you feel about this true story?